D1083279

It Must Be Hard to be a Mother

by
Rosalind Welcher

published by

Panda Prints, Inc.   New York

It must be hard to be a MOTHER

a mother has so many things to do

She has to see that you eat all
the things that you're supposed
to eat

She has to make you go
to bed on time

... and bRush youR teeth

and wash youR FaCe

and put your clothes away

She has to hold you in her lap
when you are little

She has to sing you lullabies
to put you to sleep....

she has to scold you when
you're naughty

She has to laugh with you when you're feeling happy

She has to comfort you
when you're feeling sad

she has to bake cakes for
you when it's your birthday

she has to hold your head
when you are feeling sick

she has to always be there
when you need her

she has to Love you No
matter what you do

it must be awfully hard
to be a mother....

but it must be sort of
WONDERFUL too

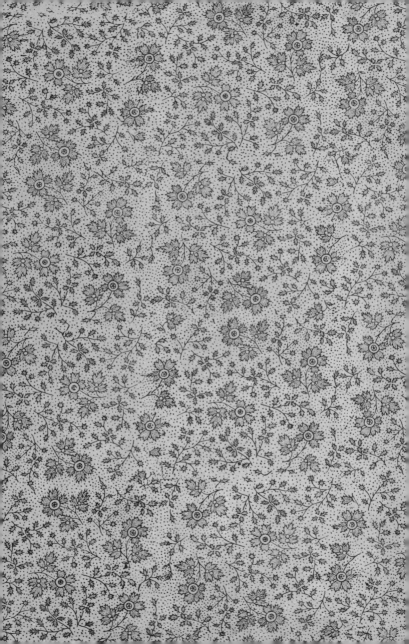

but it must be sort of
WONDERFUL too

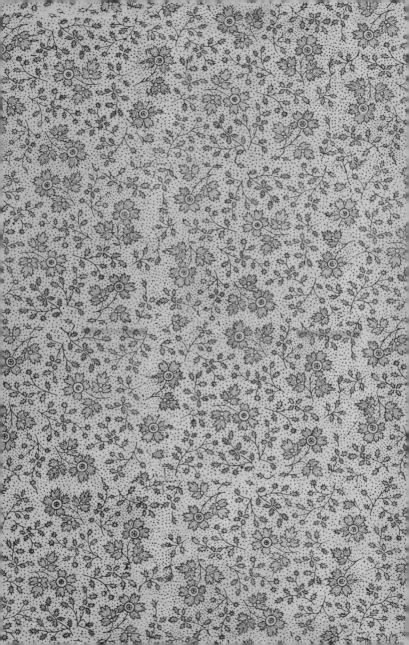

but it must be sort of
WONDERFUL too

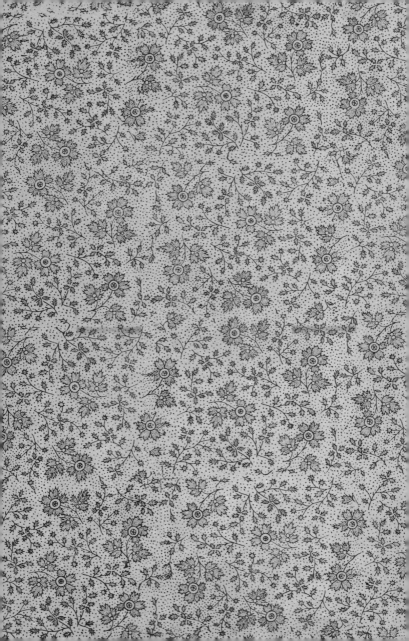